Emma Hobrough

Music Theory in Practice

Grade 4

GW00419455

ERIC TAYLOR

Emma.

Valpontin@ukonline.co.uk.

Do e-mail me when
you get your result (I don't
have your e-mail
ad!)
r let me know how
you are getting on when
you get to Marlborough.

The Associated Board of the Royal Schools of Music

It's been great teaching you!
Mrs. P x

DO NOT
PHOTOCOPY
© MUSIC

3.95

Syllabus for Grade 4

As in preceding grades, with the addition of:

(1) All simple and compound duple, triple and quadruple time signatures, and the grouping of notes and rests within these times. The breve and its equivalent rest. Double-dotted notes and rests. Duplets. Questions will include the composition of a four-bar rhythm *or* (at candidate's choice) the composition of a rhythm to given words.

(2) Alto clef (C clef centred on 3rd line). The identification of notes in the alto clef in any of the keys set for this grade, and the transcription at the unison of a simple melody from the treble or the bass clef to the alto clef, and vice versa. Double sharp and double flat signs, and their cancellation. Enharmonic equivalents.

(3) Scales and key signatures of all major and minor keys up to and including five sharps and flats, with both forms of minor scales. Technical names for the notes of the diatonic scale (tonic, supertonic etc.). Construction of the chromatic scale. All intervals, not exceeding an octave, between any two diatonic notes in any of the keys set for this grade.

(4) The identification and writing of triads (root position) on the tonic, subdominant and dominant notes in any of the keys set for this grade. The recognition of $\frac{5}{3}$ (root position) chords on the tonic, subdominant and dominant notes in any of the keys set for this grade (the harmonic form of the scale will be used in minor keys).

(5) More terms and signs, including the recognition and naming (but not writing out) of the trill, turn, upper and lower mordent, acciaccatura and appoggiatura. Questions about a passage of music will include simple related questions about standard orchestral instruments.

First published in 1990 by
The Associated Board of the Royal Schools of Music (Publishing) Ltd
Reprinted in 1990, 1991, 1992, 1995, 1996, 1997, 1998, 1999, 2000, 2001, 2002, 2003, 2004, 2005
© 1990 by The Associated Board of the Royal Schools of Music
ISBN 1 85472 493 2

All rights reserved. No part of this publication may be reproduced,
stored in a retrieval system, or transmitted in any form or by any means,
electronic, mechanical, photocopying, recording, or otherwise,
without the prior permission of the copyright owner.

Typesetting and music processing by Halstan & Co. Ltd, Amersham, Bucks
Printed in Great Britain by Headley Brothers Ltd, Ashford, Kent

Contents

Thanks are due to the following for permission to reprint extracts
from copyright works: Boosey & Hawkes Music Publishers Ltd;
Breitkopf & Härtel; Consolidated Music Publishers/Dorsey Brothers
Music Ltd; Edition Wilhelm Hansen AS; Alfred Lengnick & Co. Ltd;
Novello & Co. Ltd; Schott & Co. Ltd; William Jay Smith; The Society
of Authors; Stainer & Bell Ltd.

The music on the cover is the opening of an arrangement
for trumpet in D and piano by Philip Cranmer of the aria,
'The trumpet shall sound', from Handel's *Messiah*
(*Handel and Bach Arias*, published by the Associated Board).

In the quoted music examples, tempo marks without brackets occur
in the original as shown. Tempo marks in brackets occur earlier in the
music or are editorial.

A Time signatures

(see *The AB Guide to Music Theory*, 1/2, 3/3 & 5/1–3)

In Grade 4, exercises may be set on all simple and compound duple, triple and quadruple time signatures. Those already introduced in the previous grades are:

Simple time $\frac{3}{8}$

$\frac{2}{4}$ $\frac{3}{4}$ $\frac{4}{4}$

$\frac{2}{2}$ $\frac{3}{2}$ $\frac{4}{2}$

Compound time $\frac{6}{8}$ $\frac{9}{8}$ $\frac{12}{8}$

Of the other possibilities, some are uncommon, e.g. $\frac{2}{8}$ (although an example is quoted in Exercise 23 below); while others are even more rarely found. Those in the following list, however, may all be met quite frequently and should be understood in Grade 4:

Simple time $\frac{4}{8}$

Compound time $\frac{6}{4}$ $\frac{9}{4}$

$\frac{6}{16}$ $\frac{9}{16}$ $\frac{12}{16}$

$\frac{4}{8}$ does not present any new problems of notation, since *on paper* there is no difference between a passage in $\frac{4}{8}$ and the same notes written in $\frac{2}{4}$. This, for example, could have a time signature of either $\frac{4}{8}$ or $\frac{2}{4}$:

although the choice of time signature should of course affect the way in which the passage is performed. $\frac{4}{8}$ indicates four beats in a bar, while $\frac{2}{4}$ indicates two beats in a bar. They only *look* the same because in $\frac{4}{8}$ the beats are written as quavers, while in $\frac{2}{4}$ they are written as crotchets.

Exercise 1   Add the upper figure to the time signature in each of these examples.

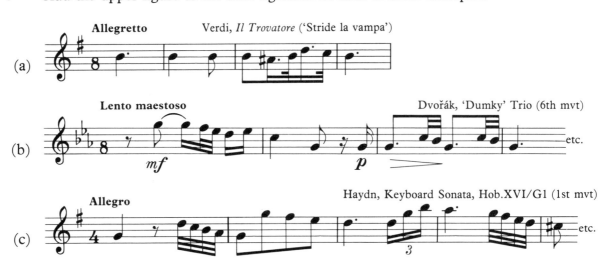

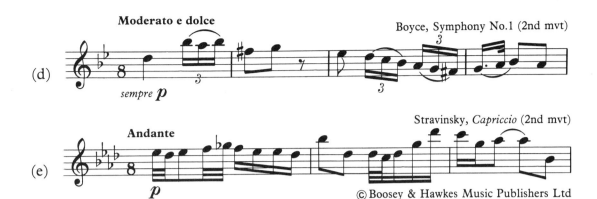

Boyce, Symphony No.1 (2nd mvt)

Stravinsky, *Capriccio* (2nd mvt)

© Boosey & Hawkes Music Publishers Ltd

Exercise 2   Rewrite this rhythm in $\frac{4}{8}$ without changing its effect (the solution to the first bar is given).

Similarly, rewrite this rhythm in $\frac{4}{4}$.

In the new compound time signatures, the grouping of notes and rests follows the rules applied to $\frac{6}{8}$, $\frac{9}{8}$ and $\frac{12}{8}$ in Grade 3. All that is different is that:

in $\frac{6}{4}$, $\frac{9}{4}$ and $\frac{12}{4}$ the note values are doubled (e.g. quavers become crotchets); and

in $\frac{6}{16}$, $\frac{9}{16}$ and $\frac{12}{16}$ the note values are halved (e.g. quavers become semiquavers).

Exercise 3   Add bar-lines to the following. Except where the first bar-line is given, each example starts on the first beat of the bar.

J. S. Bach, 48 Preludes & Fugues, Bk II (Fugue No.4)

Howells, *Psalm Preludes for organ*, Op.32 No.1

© Novello & Co. Ltd

Exercise 3
(continued)

Exercise 4

Rewrite each of the following, using the given time signatures but without changing the effect. (As an illustration, the solution to the first example is given.)

Exercise 5   Add the time signature to each of the following.

© Breitkopf & Härtel

Exercise 5
(continued)

(e) Lento — Vaughan Williams, *A London Symphony* (1st mvt)

ppp

©Stainer & Bell Ltd

(f) J. S. Bach, 48 Preludes & Fugues, Bk II (Prelude No.21)

The passages quoted in Exercises 4 and 5 above provide examples of the ways in which notes and rests should be grouped in the new time signatures. It must always be made as clear as possible where the beat occurs. Remember that in compound time the beat is always a *dotted* note: e.g. in $\frac{6}{4}$ a dotted minim; in $\frac{6}{16}$ a dotted quaver. Thus the first three bars of the Brahms melody (Exercise 4c) are written as shown there, and NOT –

(This last notation is wrong because it implies three minim beats in a bar, i.e. a time signature of $\frac{3}{2}$.) And in Exercise 4d, by Handel, notice that the semiquavers were beamed together in threes, to show the dotted quaver beat. Had they been beamed in sixes –

the notation would have suggested a time signature of $\frac{6}{8}$. In Exercise 3e, Debussy's beaming is another way of showing that the semiquavers are grouped in threes, and therefore that the beat is again a dotted quaver.

Exercise 6 Copy out the following, putting in bar-lines in accordance with the time signatures. Beam notes together as appropriate, and correct the notation of notes and rests where necessary. (As an illustration, the solution to the first example is given.) Except where the first bar-line is given, each example starts on the first beat of the bar.

(a) **(Adagio molto)** — Beethoven, Piano Sonata, Op.111 (2nd mvt)

p

(Adagio molto)

p

(b) **Andante** Wagner, *The Flying Dutchman* (Overture)

(c) **(Andante)** Handel, Concerto Grosso, Op.6 No.3 (2nd mvt)

(d) **(Allegro)** Hindemith, *Ludus Tonalis* ('Interludium')

etc.

Copyright 1943 by Associated Music Publishers, Inc., New York. Copyright 1943 by Schott & Co. Ltd, London. Copyright assigned to B. Schott's Söhne 1968. Reproduced by permission.

(e) **Allegro molto moderato** Sibelius, Symphony No.7

© Edition Wilhelm Hansen AS

(f) **Allegro** J. S. Bach, Flute Sonata No.1, BWV 1030

etc.

B   Alto clef

(see *The AB Guide to Music Theory*, 4/7)

The C clef is printed 𝄡 , but it can be drawn more simply, e.g. 𝄡, 𝄡 or 𝄡 . What is essential is that the two curved lines should be clearly placed above and below a stave line: the stave line runs *between* them and always indicates middle C. When the clef is centred on the middle line of the stave –

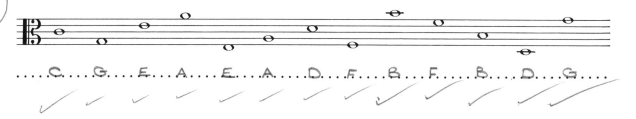

it is known as the 'alto' clef. This clef is now used mainly by the viola, but in earlier periods it had a wider use, especially in vocal music.

Exercise 7   Underneath each of these notes, write its letter name.

....C.....G.....E.....A.....E.....A.....D.....F.....B.....F.....B.....D.....G....

In previous grades, key signatures of up to four sharps or flats were introduced. They are laid out thus in the alto clef:

Exercise 8   After each clef, write the key signature and tonic triad of the key named.

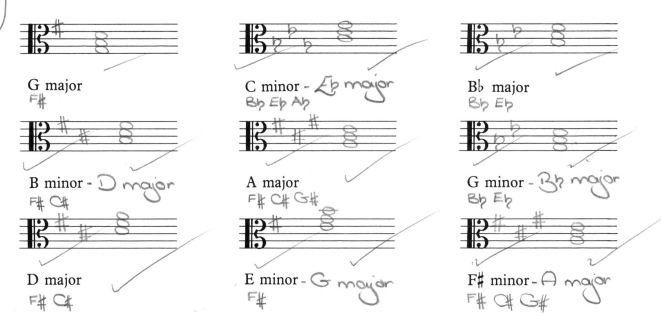

G major
F#

C minor - Eb major
Bb Eb Ab

Bb major
Bb Eb

B minor - D major
F# C#

A major
F# C# G#

G minor - Bb major
Bb Eb

D major
F# C#

E minor - G major
F#

F# minor - A major
F# C# G#

at the same pitch.

Exercise 9 Rewrite the following, using the alto clef.

Retake to middle C.

Exercise 10 Rewrite the following, using the given clefs.

Retake to mid C!!

© Copyright 1947 by Hawkes & Son (London) Ltd
Reproduced by permission of Boosey & Hawkes Music Publishers Ltd.

C Double sharps and double flats

(see *The AB Guide to Music Theory*, 4/5)

Exercise 11 Under each of these notes, write its full name (for example, 'C double sharp').

G double. sharp   B. double. flat   E double flat   F. double. sharp

Exercise 12 After each of these notes, write two other notes which sound the same (i.e. notes which are enharmonic equivalents of the given note), as shown in the first example.

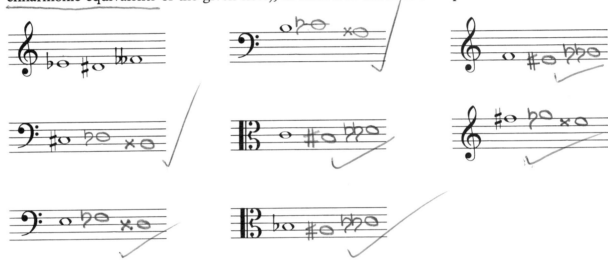

The next exercise deals with the cancellation of double sharps and double flats.

Exercise 13 Before each of the notes marked *, add the accidental needed to restore it to its normal pitch (as shown by the key signature).

(a)

(b)

(c)

(d)

D Breves, double dots, duplets

(see *The AB Guide to Music Theory,* 1/1, 3/1–2, 5/4)

A breve, ‖○‖ , lasts as long as two semibreves. It fills a whole bar in $\frac{4}{2}$.

A breve rest is written ▭ , and this rest is used for a completely silent bar in $\frac{4}{2}$.

(Remember, however, that in all other time signatures a completely silent bar is shown as ▬ .)

Exercise 14   Rewrite these scales, doubling the time values. (The opening of the first one is given.)

Exercise 15   Rewrite these scales, halving the time values. Remember to alter the time signatures accordingly.

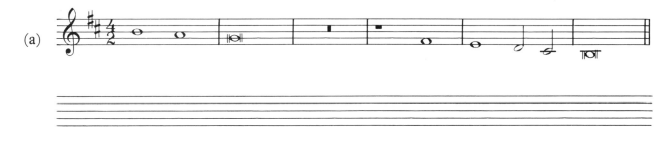

A second dot after a note adds half the length already added by the first dot –

e.g.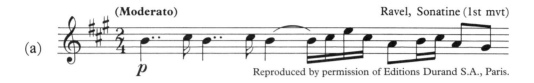

Exercise 16 Add the missing bar-lines in the following. Each example starts on the first beat of the bar, except where the first bar-line is given.

(a)

(Moderato)   Ravel, Sonatine (1st mvt)

p   Reproduced by permission of Editions Durand S.A., Paris.

(b)

(Maestoso)   Wagner, *Götterdämmerung* (Siegfried's Funeral Music)

(c)

Adagio   Beethoven, Piano Sonata, Op.31 No.2 (2nd mvt)

p dolce

A duplet is most commonly indicated by a figure *2* above the notes: for example,

♩. divided into two becomes

♩. divided into two becomes

♪. divided into two becomes

Notice the time values in the above illustrations.[1]

Duplets may also be written as dotted notes: for example,

♩. divided into two becomes

♩. divided into two becomes

♪. divided into two becomes

Exercise 17 Add bar-lines in the following, all of which begin on the first beat of the bar.

(a)

♩. = 78   Lalo, *Symphonie Espagnole* (5th mvt)

[1]Very occasionally, duplets are written with other time values (see *The AB Guide to Music Theory*, Part I, p.104), but these are too rare to be regarded as standard practice. They should not be used in the theory examinations.

Exercise 18   Without changing the effect, rewrite the following, using the given time signatures.
(As an illustration, the opening of the first example is given.)

Reproduced by permission of Editions Durand S.A., Paris.

June 30.

E Keys with five sharps or flats
Technical names of notes in diatonic scales

(see *The AB Guide to Music Theory*, 4/1–4)

Grade 4 adds major and minor scales with five sharps or flats:

B major G♯ minor D♭ major B♭ minor

The key signatures are laid out thus:

Exercise 19 Write accidentals where they are needed to make the scales named. (Do not use key signatures.) Add ⌐‾‾¬ above any pairs of notes which are a semitone apart.

B major

B♭ melodic minor

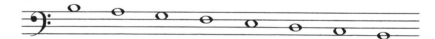

D♭ major

G♯ harmonic minor

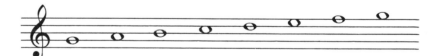

B♭ melodic minor

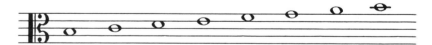

Try in hols.

Exercise 20 Write the clefs and accidentals needed to make the scales named. (Do not use key signatures.) Add ⌐‾‾¬ above any pairs of notes which are a semitone apart.

B♭ harmonic minor

B major

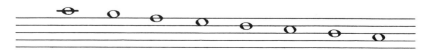

Db major

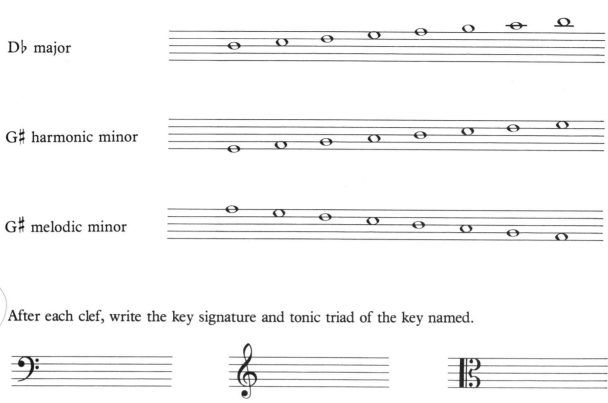

G# harmonic minor

G# melodic minor

Exercise 21 After each clef, write the key signature and tonic triad of the key named.

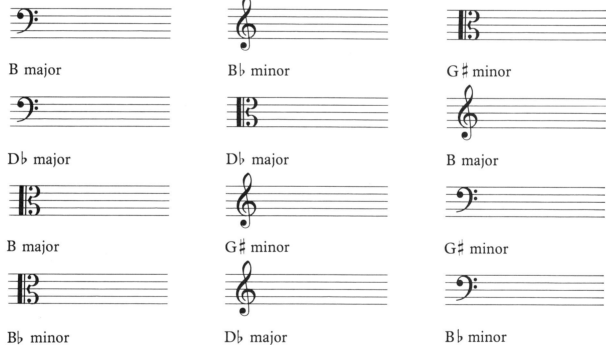

B major | Bb minor | G# minor

Db major | Db major | B major

B major | G# minor | G# minor

Bb minor | Db major | Bb minor

Exercise 22 Name the key of each of the following. Then write them out again, using the correct key signature. Leave out any accidentals which become unnecessary, but remember also to add any that may be needed.

Adagio un poco mosso   Beethoven, Piano Concerto No.5 ('Emperor') (2nd mvt)

(a)

Key . . . .

Exercise 22
(continued)

(b) Andantino — Tchaikovsky, Symphony No.4 (2nd mvt)

Key . . . .

(c) J. S. Bach, 48 Preludes & Fugues, Bk I (Prelude No.18)

Key . . . .

(d) Allegretto — Beethoven, Piano Sonata, Op.10 No.2 (2nd mvt)

Key . . . .

(e) ♩ = 72 — Stravinsky, *Firebird* ('Ronde des Princesses')

©Schott & Co. Ltd

Key . . . .

(f) Andante sostenuto ♩ = 52 — Berlioz, *Roman Carnival* (Overture)

Key . . . .

[handwritten top margin: Copy — I have put these in your yellow bk. for ref. H]

In Grade 4, candidates are also required to know the technical names of the notes forming major and minor scales, i.e. the names of the 'degrees' of diatonic scales. These, in ascending order, are:

[handwritten: LEARN] ‖ (1) Tonic, (2) Supertonic, (3) Mediant, (4) Subdominant, (5) Dominant, (6) Submediant, (7) Leading note, (8) Tonic. ‖

Exercise 23 Name the key of each of the following, and underneath write the technical names (e.g. tonic, dominant) of the notes marked 1, 2, 3 and 4.

[handwritten left margin: Try in hols. e.g.]

[handwritten right margin: Always count up from tonic i.e. G → F# = 7]

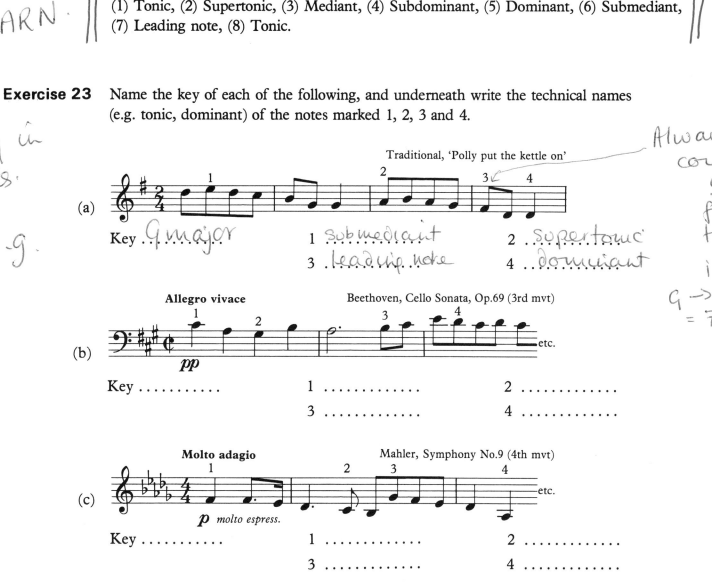

(a) Key ...G major...   1 ...submediant...   2 ...supertonic...
3 ...leading note...   4 ...dominant...

(b) Key ....   1 ....   2 ....
3 ....   4 ....

(c) Key ....   1 ....   2 ....
3 ....   4 ....

(d) Key ....   1 ....   2 ....
3 ....   4 ....

(e) Key ....   1 ....   2 ....
3 ....   4 ....

Exercise 23
(continued)

Berlioz, *The Damnation of Faust* (Serenade)

(f)

Key . . . . 1 . . . . 2 . . . .
3 . . . . 4 . . . .

Tchaikovsky, Symphony No.4 (1st mvt)

(g)

Key . . . . 1 . . . . 2 . . . .
3 . . . . 4 . . . .

Liszt, Piano Concerto No.2 (1st mvt)

(h)

Key . . . . 1 . . . . 2 . . . .
3 . . . . 4 . . . .

F Four-bar rhythms

Some suggestions concerning the ways in which a four-bar rhythm might be planned were made in *Music Theory in Practice*, Grades 2 and 3. In Grade 4, nothing needs to be added to those general rules, but they must now be applied to the new rhythms and time signatures.

Exercise 24 Compose four-bar rhythms beginning as follows.

(c)

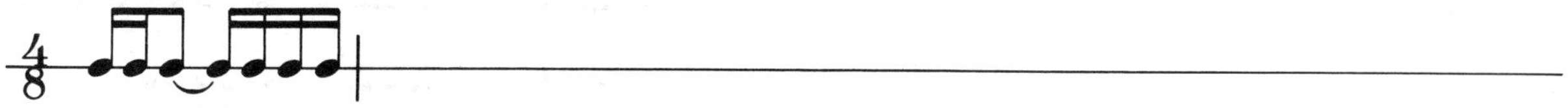

(d)

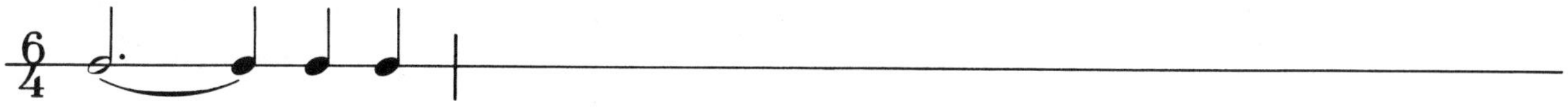

(e)

(f)

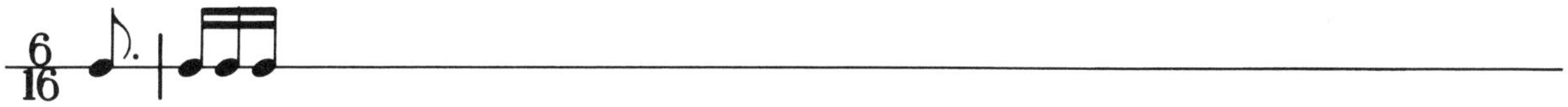

(g)

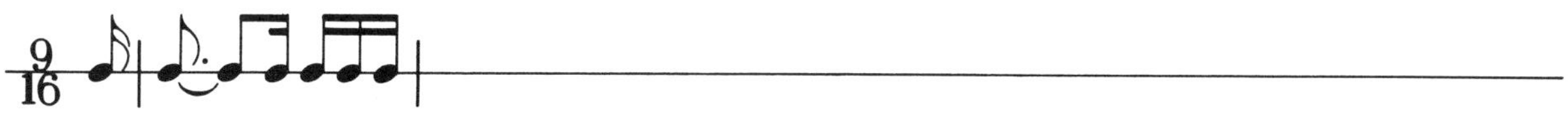

(h)

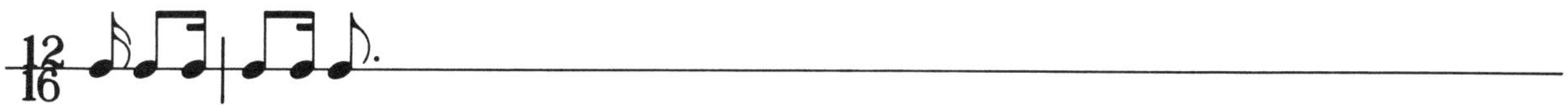

Exercise 25   Use each of the following in a four-bar rhythm, though not necessarily at the beginning.

(a)   a breve in $\frac{4}{2}$

(b)   a triplet in $\frac{4}{8}$

(c)   a duplet in $\frac{9}{8}$

(d)   two consecutive crotchet rests in $\frac{6}{4}$

(e)   a double-dotted minim in $\frac{4}{4}$

(f)   a note tied over a bar-line in $\frac{9}{16}$

G Triads and chords on I, IV and V

(see *The AB Guide to Music Theory*, 8/1–2)

In earlier grades, the only triad included was that on the tonic, the first degree of the scale. In Grade 4, candidates should also be able to recognise and write triads on the 4th and 5th degrees, i.e. the subdominant and dominant triads, e.g. –

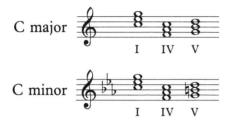

These three triads – tonic, subdominant, dominant – are the 'primary' triads of the key. They can be indicated by roman numerals: I, IV and V respectively.

It is important to remember that the dominant triad in a minor key requires an accidental: the third of the chord has to be raised a semitone, since it is the leading note of the scale. Hence the B♮ in the above example. Similarly, the dominant triad of A minor is:

Exercise 26 After each of the following clefs, write the key signature of the given key, followed by the three primary triads: tonic, subdominant, dominant. Identify the triads by writing I, IV or V underneath.

G major ....

D minor ....

D♭ major ....

F♯ minor ....

E major ....

G♯ minor ....

Exercise 27   Identify each of these triads by writing I, IV or V underneath.

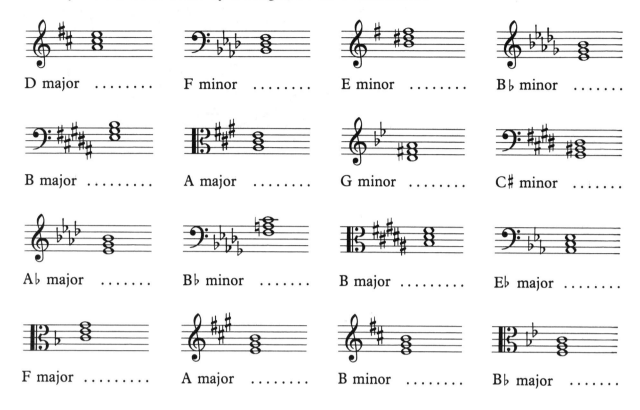

D major ....   F minor ....   E minor ....   B♭ minor ....

B major ....   A major ....   G minor ....   C♯ minor ....

A♭ major ....   B♭ minor ....   B major ....   E♭ major ....

F major ....   A major ....   B minor ....   B♭ major ....

Exercise 28   Write triads as indicated in the given keys. Do not use key signatures, but add the necessary accidentals before notes which need them.

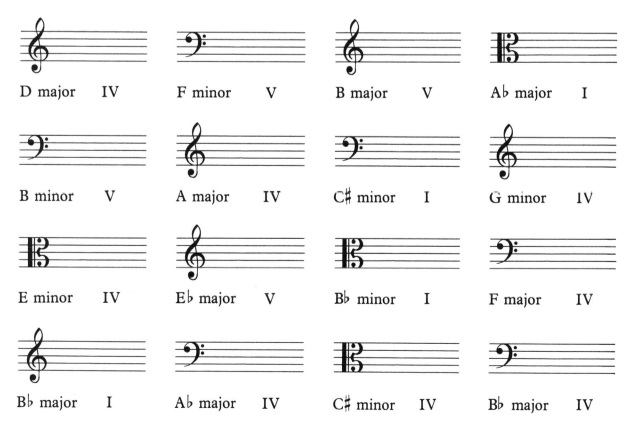

D major   IV   F minor   V   B major   V   A♭ major   I

B minor   V   A major   IV   C♯ minor   I   G minor   IV

E minor   IV   E♭ major   V   B♭ minor   I   F major   IV

B♭ major   I   A♭ major   IV   C♯ minor   IV   B♭ major   IV

You may also be asked to recognise (though not to write) chords made from the notes of the three primary triads. Again, they can be indicated by I, IV and V. The lowest note of the triad, its 'root', will always be at the bottom (i.e. the chords will be 'in root position') in this grade.

Exercise 29 Name the key of each of these passages, and identify each of the chords marked * by writing I, IV or V underneath.

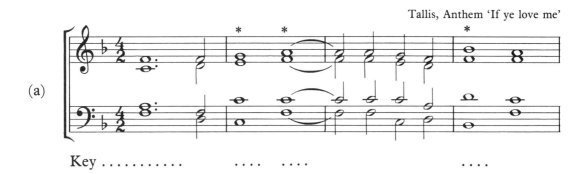

(a)

Key . . . .

(b)

Key . . . .

(c)

Key . . . .

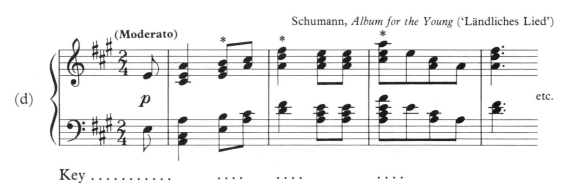

(d)

Key . . . .

(e) Tchaikovsky, *Album for the Young* ('The Doll's Funeral')

Adagio

Key ....

(f) Grieg, *Watchman's Song*, Op.12 No.3

Molto andante e semplice

etc.

Key ....

(g) Beethoven, Piano Sonata, Op.57 (2nd mvt)

Andante con moto

etc.

Key ....

(h) J. S. Bach, Chorale 'Es woll uns Gott'

etc.

Key ....

(i) Schumann, *Piano Sonata for the Young*, Op.118 No.1 (1st mvt)

(Allegro)

etc.

Key ....

H Intervals

(see *The AB Guide to Music Theory*, 7/1)

You may be asked to name the interval between *any* two notes in the major and minor scales set for this grade (see Section E). The lower note will not necessarily be the key-note, but the interval will not be larger than an octave.

Consider, for example, the intervals between consecutive notes in the scale of C major:

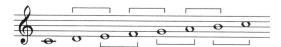

These must all be 2nds of some kind. But what kind?

Start by seeing whether both notes occur in a major scale, with the lower note as the key-note. Take the D–E above, for example. E is the 2nd degree of the scale of D major, so the interval is a major 2nd. Similarly:

F–G is a major 2nd (G being the 2nd degree of the scale of F major)
G–A is a major 2nd (A being the 2nd degree of the scale of G major)
A–B is a major 2nd (B being the 2nd degree of the scale of A major)

However, this will not work with E–F, since F(♮) is not found in the scale of E major. (The E major scale starts E–F♯). There are other intervals between notes in major scales which present similar problems, and many more in the harmonic and melodic minor scales. But all the problems can be solved by remembering these rules:

When a major interval is made a semitone larger, it becomes augmented.
When a major interval is made a semitone smaller, it becomes minor.

When a minor interval is made a semitone larger, it becomes major.
When a minor interval is made a semitone smaller, it becomes diminished.

When a perfect interval is made a semitone larger, it becomes augmented.
When a perfect interval is made a semitone smaller, it becomes diminished.

This summary may make the rules easier to remember:

(largest)	augmented	major	augmented
	MAJOR	MINOR	PERFECT
(smallest)	minor	diminished	diminished

Now we can solve the problem which we had with E–F(♮) in the C major scale. If the notes had been E–F *sharp*, there would have been no difficulty: F♯ is the 2nd degree of the scale of E major, so the interval would have been a major 2nd. However, F♮ is a semitone lower than F♯: the interval is therefore a semitone smaller. Consequently, major becomes minor, and E–F♮ is a minor 2nd.

The same thing happens with the interval from B–C. B–C cannot be a *major* 2nd, because the scale of B major starts B–C♯. C♮ is a semitone lower than C♯, so B–C(♮) is a *minor* 2nd again. (Notice that it is not sufficient to describe B–C as a 'semitone'.)

Here is another example which occurs in the key of C major (and also in C minor):

With F as a key-note, the 4th degree of the scale would normally be B♭. F–B♭ is a perfect 4th. But the B♭ has been raised a semitone (to B♮), so the interval has become larger, and perfect becomes augmented: F–B♮ is an augmented 4th.

There is another way of altering an interval. Instead of raising or lowering the *top* note, the *bottom* note can be raised or lowered. If you raise the bottom note of an interval, you make the interval smaller. If you lower the bottom note, the interval becomes larger. So the above rules still apply. Consider, for example, this interval, which occurs in B minor:

It is hard to think of A♯ as a key-note. But if it had been A *natural*, there would have been no difficulty: A–D is a perfect 4th. Raising the A to A♯ makes the interval a semitone smaller, and perfect becomes diminished: A♯–D is a diminished 4th.

Exercise 30 Give the full names (e.g. 'major 6th', 'augmented 4th') of the following intervals. (Remember the key signatures.)

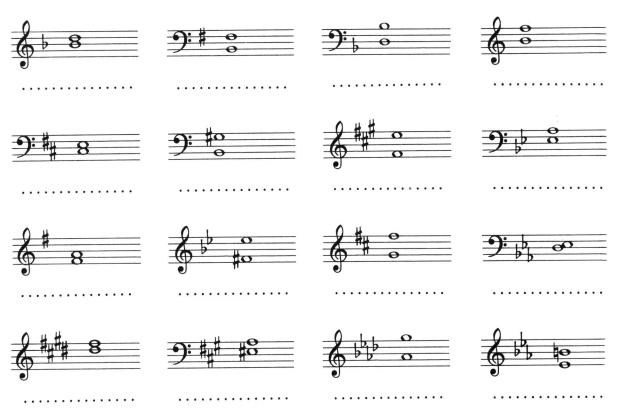

Exercise 30
(continued)

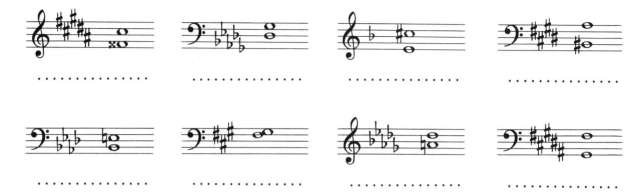

Exercise 31 Name the intervals marked ⌐——¬ in the following. Remember that an interval is always calculated from the lower of the two notes, regardless of which comes first.

▌ Writing a rhythm to words

(see *The AB Guide to Music Theory*, 6)

Note that you will always have a choice between writing a rhythm to words and writing a four-bar rhythm (as in Section F).

In Grade 4, you will be asked to write only a *rhythm* to words, not a complete melody. Use the modern method of notation, i.e. quavers and shorter notes should be beamed together where suitable, even when set to different syllables (not written separately, as used to be the custom).

Usually the words given will be in verse form, e.g. –

Gone were but the winter cold,
And gone were but the snow,
I could sleep in the wild woods
Where primroses blow.
                Allan Cunningham

First, read the verse carefully. Think about its meaning; and then decide which are the strong (stressed) syllables, and which are the weak. The first two lines above, for example, seem to have alternate syllables stressed: it may be helpful to mark them with accent signs –

Góne were bút the wínter cóld,
And góne were bút the snów,

This almost automatically produces a duple-time rhythm, e.g. $\frac{2}{4}$. All that is required is to set each syllable to a crotchet, and then to put each stressed crotchet in a strong position by making it the first beat of a bar –

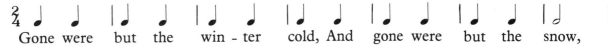

Gone were but the win - ter cold, And gone were but the snow,

The third line, however, is not so easy. If we were to accent alternate syllables, as in the first two lines –

Í could sléep in thé wild wóods

we would get a stress on 'the'. But 'the' is an unimportant word, which certainly should not be stressed. And continuing into the fourth line, we would get a stress on the last syllable of 'primroses' –

Where prímrosés blow.

But this is also wrong: 'primroses' is pronounced with only one stress – on the *first* syllable.

A little thought about the meaning of the words, and how they should be pronounced, shows that the correct accentuation must be –

I could sléep in the wíld wóods
Where prímroses blów.

This is not nearly so regular as the first two lines, but we can still keep the stressed syllables on the strong beats by using some longer and some shorter notes –

Now we have seven bars for the first two lines, and seven for the last two: fourteen bars in all. This is not impossible, but a total of sixteen bars (eight + eight) would be much more usual. And indeed the ear seems to expect a long note at the end of the second line of the verse and again at the end of the fourth, which would give us a 'regular' sixteen-bar phrase:

(Version 1)

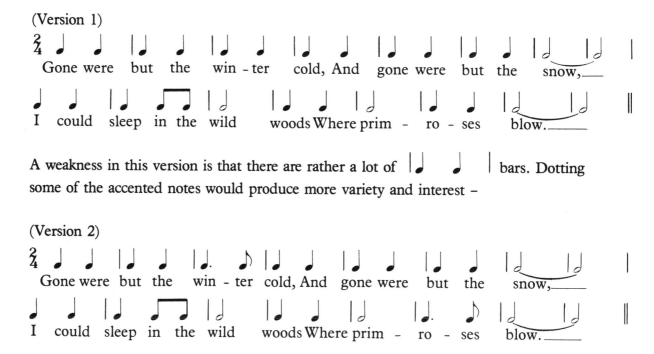

A weakness in this version is that there are rather a lot of ♩♩ bars. Dotting some of the accented notes would produce more variety and interest –

(Version 2)

Notice that the verse does not *have* to be set in duple time. By lengthening the strong syllables, it could equally well be set in triple time –

(Version 3)

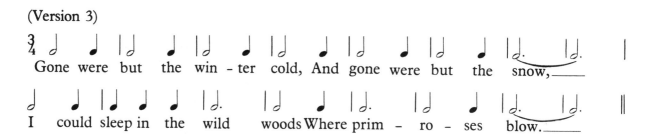

The trouble with all the versions so far is that there are too many equally-stressed syllables, with the result that the most important words do not sufficiently stand out. A careful reading of the verse may suggest that the most important words are 'gone', 'cold', 'snow', 'sleep', 'wild', 'primroses' and 'blow'. We could highlight them by putting *only* these words on the first beat of a bar. If we draw the corresponding bar-lines into the text, we can begin to see the effect –

| *Gone were but the winter* | *cold,*
And | *gone were but the* | *snow,*
I could | *sleep in the* | *wild woods*
Where | *primroses* | *blow.*

This is only an outline but it can be used in many ways –

(Version 4)

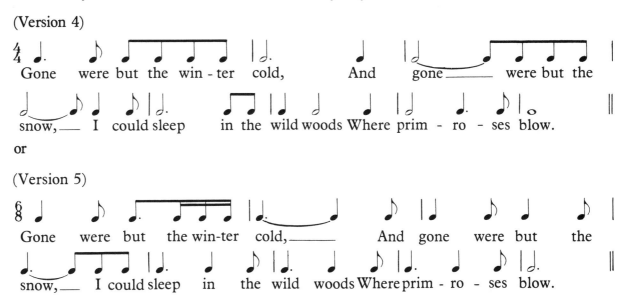

or

(Version 5)

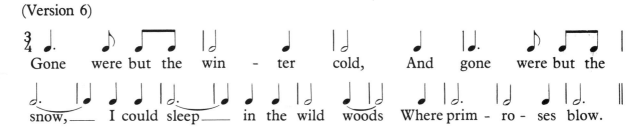

As it happens, the last two versions above both form regular eight-bar phrases. But there is no necessity for your word rhythms always to be in eight or sixteen bars. This, for example, is in thirteen bars, yet it still fits the natural stresses and meaning of the words –

(Version 6)

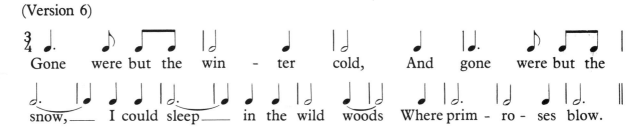

For further illustration of the points made on the previous pages, four workings are given below of the opening lines of 'The Owl and the Pussy-Cat' by Edward Lear –

The Owl and the Pussy-cat went to sea
  In a beautiful pea-green boat,
They took some honey, and plenty of money,
  Wrapped up in a five-pound note.

The first two versions are adequate though somewhat basic, but the third and fourth are more interesting and varied.

Here are some points about how words are placed under the music.

(1) *Every* syllable needs a note. This may seem obvious, but people do sometimes make the mistake of writing, for example –

money and

This is impossible: 'money' cannot be sung to a single note. It has two syllables, and therefore it must have two notes –

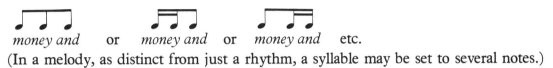

money and   or   money and   or   money and   etc.

(In a melody, as distinct from just a rhythm, a syllable may be set to several notes.)

(2) Each syllable is placed under the note to which it is to be sung. Where possible, the first letter goes under the note; but this is not essential, provided it is clear which syllable belongs to which note.

(3) Some syllables have more letters than others (compare 'a' and 'wrapped' in the verse by Lear) and thus need more space. Do not write out the music in full first, leaving the words to be fitted in later, or you may find you do not have enough room for them.

(4) On the other hand, a word of two or more syllables may have to be spaced out, if the notes above it are not to be squashed too close together. This can be done by adding a hyphen (-) between the syllables, e.g. prim-ro-ses. More than one hyphen may be used if necessary (prim - - ro - - ses). The word itself is divided so that each syllable begins with a consonant where possible (prim-ro-ses, *not* prim-ros-es *or* pri-mro-ses).

(5) When a word of one syllable, or the last syllable of a word, is fitted to two or more notes (including tied notes), its duration should be shown by a continuous line after it, not a hyphen, (e.g. boat, _____). Notice that, if there is a punctuation mark (such as a comma) after the word, it goes *before* the line, not at the end.

Exercise 32   Compose rhythms for the words on the next three pages. Make more than one working of each verse, experimenting with different time signatures (simple or compound; duple, triple or quadruple). Write the notes on the continuous lines and the words on the dotted lines below.

One road leads to London,
One road leads to Wales,
My road leads me seawards
To the white dipping sails.   *John Masefield*

Reproduced by permission of The Society of Authors
as the literary representative of the Estate of John Masefield.

A silver-scaled Dragon with jaws flaming red
Sits at my elbow and toasts my bread.   *William Jay Smith*

From LAUGHING TIME: *Nonsense Poems* by William Jay Smith, published by
Delacorte Press, 1980. © 1955, 1957, 1980 by William Jay Smith. Reproduced by permission of
William Jay Smith.

I remember, I remember,
The house where I was born,
The little window where the sun
Came peeping in at morn.   *Thomas Hood*

She's like the swallow that flies so high,
She's like the river that never runs dry.   *Traditional*

Home is the sailor, home from sea
And the hunter home from the hill.   *Robert Louis Stevenson*

_____

. . . .

_____

. . . .

_____

. . . .

_____

. . . .

_____

. . . .

_____

. . . .

The earth was green, the sky was blue:
  I saw and heard one sunny morn
A skylark hang between the two
  A singing speck above the corn.   *Christina Rossetti*

_____

. . . .

_____

. . . .

_____

. . . .

_____

. . . .

_____

. . . .

J The chromatic scale

(see *The AB Guide to Music Theory*, 4/6)

You may be asked to write a chromatic scale. It could be with or without a key signature and ascending or descending (or both). Chromatic scales can be written in many different ways, but all you need remember is to make sure that for every line and space there is at least one note, but not more than two[1]. For example, if you were asked to write an ascending chromatic scale, starting on the key-note of A♭ major and using the key signature, any of the following would be acceptable answers:

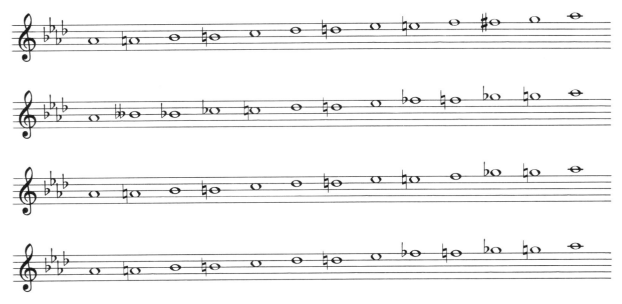

Normally, the unaltered dominant and subdominant notes are among those included (e.g. the E♭s and the D♭s in the scales above).

Exercise 33 Starting with the first note as given, turn each of the following into chromatic scales by adding the accidentals which are needed. Do not include unnecessary accidentals.

[1]The question will not ask you to use either the 'harmonic' or the 'melodic' form of the chromatic scale.

Exercise 33
(continued)

Exercise 34 Starting with the first note as given, turn each of the following into chromatic scales by adding the accidentals which are needed. Note the key signatures, and do not include unnecessary accidentals.

Exercise 35 Write chromatic scales as described, using the given rhythms. Do not include unnecessary accidentals.

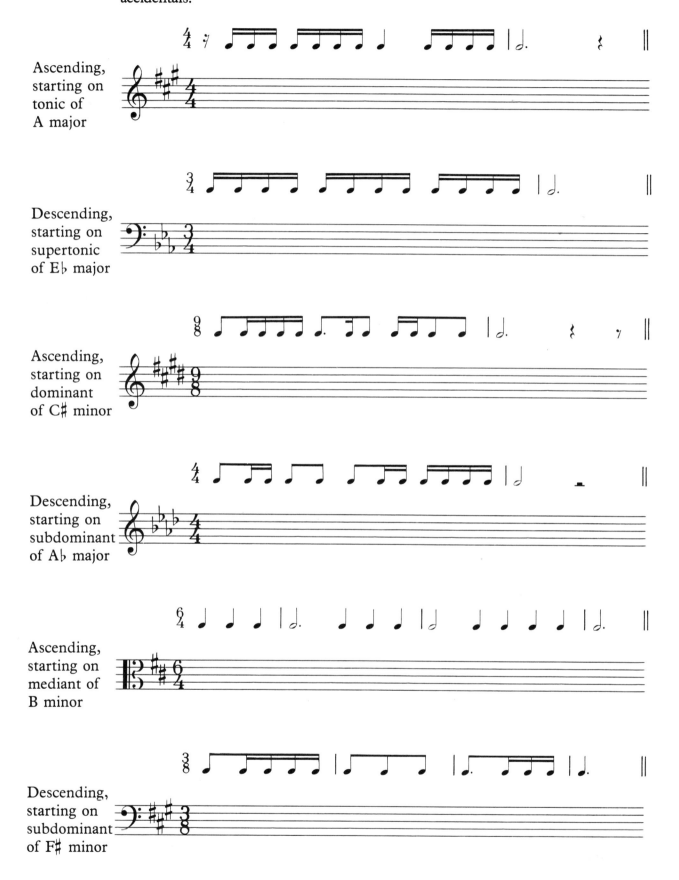

K Ornaments

(see *The AB Guide to Music Theory*, 12)

You may be asked to recognise and to name various ornament signs. These are the trill, turn, upper and lower mordent, acciaccatura and appoggiatura. Note the following.

(1)   The trill is also known as a 'shake', and you may use that word instead.
It will be shown in this grade by *tr*, with or without a wavy line after it.

(2)   The turn which will be used in Grade 4 is sometimes called the 'upper turn': ∾ .
Remember that it is important to distinguish between a turn immediately *over* a note and one *between* notes.

(3)   To prevent misunderstanding, you should use the terms 'upper mordent' (meaning ∿) and 'lower mordent' (meaning ∿) in full.[1]

(4)   The acciaccatura, ♪ , is a single grace note (grace notes may also be used in groups of two or more). It is also known as a 'crushed note'. If you prefer, you may use either of the terms 'grace note' or 'crushed note' instead of acciaccatura – but if you *do* use the Italian word, remember that it has four letter c's.
Note, also, that it is always written with the stem going upwards.

(5)   'Appoggiatura' has two letter p's and two g's. You may like to think of it as a 'leaning note' (which is what the Italian word means), but do not describe it in this way in the examination.

You should, of course, understand what the ornament signs stand for, although in Grade 4 you will not be asked to write out ornamented notes in full.

Exercise 36   (a)   Add the sign for a trill (shake) above the notes marked ↑ .

(b)   Add the sign for a turn (i.e. upper turn) at the places marked ↑ .

[1]'Mordent' by itself is open to confusion, since in the past it has been used in entirely opposite senses. Strictly speaking, it (or the German *Mordant*) means the 'lower' mordent: ∿ . See *The AB Guide to Music Theory*, Part I, pp.93/4.

(c) Add the sign for an upper mordent above the notes marked ↑ .

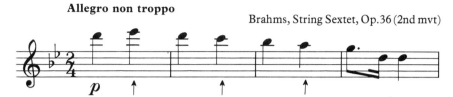

(d) Add the sign for a lower mordent above the notes marked ↑ .

(e) Write an acciaccatura before, and a note higher than, each of the notes marked ↑ .

Exercise 37   Underneath each of the following, tick which you think is the best way (i, ii, iii or iv) of playing the passage marked ⌐⎯⌐ .

Exercise 37
(continued)

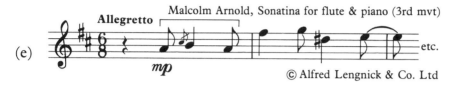

© Alfred Lengnick & Co. Ltd

Exercise 38 Underneath each of the ornament signs in the following, write the name of the sign.

L Instruments

The general questions about a passage of music may include simple, related questions about standard orchestral instruments. You should be aware of the orchestral families to which the main instruments belong.

strings: violin, viola, cello, double bass;
woodwind: flute, oboe, clarinet, bassoon;
brass: horn, trumpet, trombone, tuba;
percussion: timpani (kettledrums), side drum, bass drum, cymbals.

You should also be aware of certain signs and directions which refer to particular instruments. The more common of these are given in section M below.

It may also help you to know about the clefs which these instruments use, although specific questions will not be asked until Grade 5 –

treble clef: violin, flute, oboe, clarinet, horn (sometimes bass clef), trumpet;
alto clef: viola (sometimes treble clef);
bass clef: cello (sometimes treble or tenor clef), double bass, bassoon,
   trombone (sometimes tenor clef), tuba.

Note that string instruments can sometimes play two notes simultaneously (or even three or four). Wind instruments, however, can play only one at a time.

M Performance directions

The following terms and signs apply only to certain instruments.

Strings   *con sordini* (or *con sord.*)   with mutes
& Brass   *senza sordini* (or *senza sord.*)   without mutes

Strings   *arco*   play with the bow (a direction after *pizzicato*)
            ⊓ and ∨ are bowing marks   (⊓ is a 'down' bow and ∨ an 'up' bow)
            ⌒ a slur over or under notes means that they are to be played in one stroke of
              the bow (either up or down)
            pizzicato   plucked
            sul G   play on the G string
            sul ponticello   play near the bridge

Piano   *una corda* (literally 'one string')   press the left pedal
          tre corde (literally 'three strings')   release the left pedal
          𝒫𝑒𝑑.   ✳   press/release the right pedal
          𝑃_____
          mano   hand (*mano sinistra* or *m.s.*: left hand; *mano destra* or *m.d.*: right hand)
                     (also used by the harp)
          ⦙   spread the notes of a chord quickly, starting from the bottom note

In Grade 4 you will be expected to know the meaning of the following Italian terms.

affettuoso	tenderly
affrettando	hurrying
amabile	amiable, pleasant
appassionato	with passion
calando	getting softer, dying away (and usually slowing down)
cantando	singing
come	as, similar to (*come prima*: as before; *come sopra*: as above)
facile	easy
fuoco	fire
giusto	proper, exact (*tempo giusto*: in strict time)
l'istesso	the same (l'istesso tempo: at the same speed)
morendo	dying away
niente	nothing
nobilmente	nobly
perdendosi	dying away
possibile	possible (*presto possibile*: as fast as possible)
quasi	as if, resembling
sonoro	resonant, with rich tone
sopra	above
sotto	below (*sotto voce*: in an undertone)
veloce	swift
voce	voice

You will also be expected to know the meaning of the following French terms.

à	to, at
animé	animated, lively
assez	enough, sufficiently
avec	with
cédez	yield, relax the speed
douce	sweet
en dehors	prominent (a direction to make a melody stand out)
et	and
légèrement	light
lent	slow
mais	but
moins	less
modéré	at a moderate speed
non	not
peu	little
plus	more
presser	hurry (*en pressant*: hurrying on)
ralentir	slow down
retenu	held back (*en retenant*: holding back, slowing a little)
sans	without
très	very
un, une	one
vif	lively
vite	quick

N General exercises

Exercise 39 Look at the following melody, and then answer the questions below.

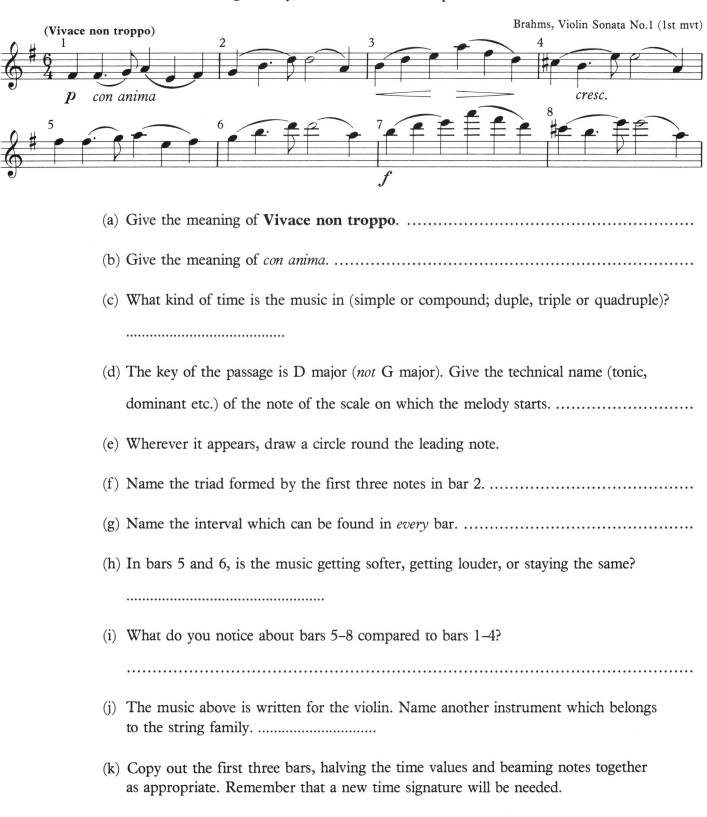

(a) Give the meaning of **Vivace non troppo**. ....

(b) Give the meaning of *con anima*. ....

(c) What kind of time is the music in (simple or compound; duple, triple or quadruple)?

   ....

(d) The key of the passage is D major (*not* G major). Give the technical name (tonic,

   dominant etc.) of the note of the scale on which the melody starts. ....

(e) Wherever it appears, draw a circle round the leading note.

(f) Name the triad formed by the first three notes in bar 2. ....

(g) Name the interval which can be found in *every* bar. ....

(h) In bars 5 and 6, is the music getting softer, getting louder, or staying the same?

   ....

(i) What do you notice about bars 5–8 compared to bars 1–4?

   ....

(j) The music above is written for the violin. Name another instrument which belongs
   to the string family. ....

(k) Copy out the first three bars, halving the time values and beaming notes together
   as appropriate. Remember that a new time signature will be needed.

Exercise 40   This melody is taken from the middle section of a Waltz by Chopin (Op.64 No.2).
Look at it, and then answer the questions below.

(a) Is the music printed above faster or slower than the music which came before it,

or is it at the same speed? .... Explain the reason for your answer.

....

(b) Add the time signature in the correct place in the music.

(c) What is the key of bars 1–12? ....

(d) Give the full name of the last note in bar 14. ....

(e) Give the full name of a note which is an enharmonic equivalent of the last note in

bar 15 (i.e. a note which *sounds* the same but is written differently). ....

(f) What is the interval between the two notes in bar 6? ....

(g) What is similar about the three passages marked ⌐*x*⌐ ⌐*y*⌐ ⌐*z*⌐ ?

....

(h) What is the name of the ornament in bar 16? ....

(i) The music includes part of a chromatic scale. Show where this begins and ends by
writing X above the first and last notes.

(j) Name a woodwind instrument which could play this melody. ....

(k) Using the alto clef, write the key signature followed by the first note of the melody.

Exercise 41 Look at this melody, and then answer the questions below.

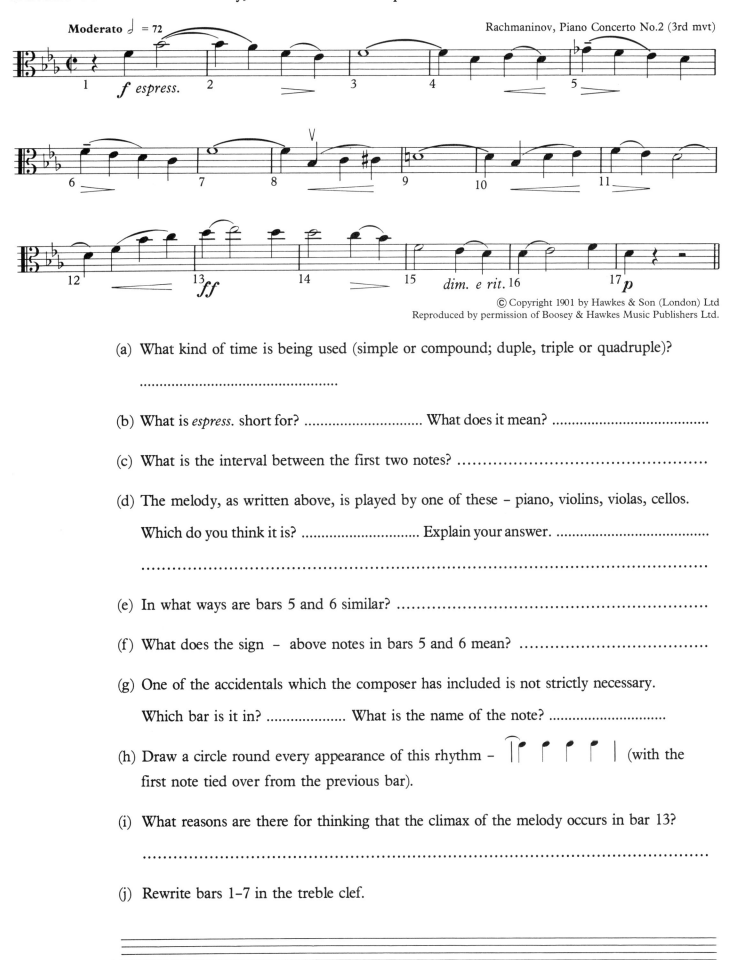

Rachmaninov, Piano Concerto No.2 (3rd mvt)

© Copyright 1901 by Hawkes & Son (London) Ltd
Reproduced by permission of Boosey & Hawkes Music Publishers Ltd.

(a) What kind of time is being used (simple or compound; duple, triple or quadruple)?

....

(b) What is *espress.* short for? .... What does it mean? ....

(c) What is the interval between the first two notes? ....

(d) The melody, as written above, is played by one of these – piano, violins, violas, cellos.

Which do you think it is? .... Explain your answer. ....

....

(e) In what ways are bars 5 and 6 similar? ....

(f) What does the sign – above notes in bars 5 and 6 mean? ....

(g) One of the accidentals which the composer has included is not strictly necessary.

Which bar is it in? .... What is the name of the note? ....

(h) Draw a circle round every appearance of this rhythm – (with the

first note tied over from the previous bar).

(i) What reasons are there for thinking that the climax of the melody occurs in bar 13?

....

(j) Rewrite bars 1–7 in the treble clef.

Exercise 42 This is a passage from the Prelude to Part I of Elgar's *The Dream of Gerontius*. Look at it and then answer the questions below.

(a) Explain the following terms:

Andantino ....

Cantando ....

molto largamente ....

(b) What kind of ornament is used in bar 1? ....

How should this note be played? ....

(c) Which of the following is the best way to play bar 11? .....

(d) Name the intervals marked ⌐‾‾ in bars 16–20.

Bar 16 ....   Bar 17 ....   Bar 18 ....

Bar 19 ....   Bar 20 ....

(e) From bar 12 to the end of the passage, the music is in D minor. Give the technical names (tonic, dominant etc.) of these notes: G (bar 12) ....

C♯ (bar 12) ....   E (bar 13) ....   B♭ (bar 13) ....

F (bar 14) ....   D (bar 15) ....   A (bar 16) ....

(f) What clues suggest that this passage is played by violins? ....

....

(g) Rewrite bars 6–10, using a compound time signature but without changing the effect.